THE ULTIMATE BIBLE SONGS COLLECTION

Early Reader Bible Story Book

Twin Sisters Productions, LLC
4710 Hudson Drive, Stow, OH 44224 USA
www.twinsisters.com   1-800-248-8946

© 2010 Twin Sisters IP, LLC
All Rights Reserved. Made in China.

ISBN-13: 978-159922-341-4

THE CREATION

Who created the little bird that sits up in the tree?

And, who created the little toad or the swinging chimpanzee?

God above, He made them all.

He made everything with care and love.

God had a plan for He even made you and me!

God made the earth.

He made the sea and He made the night and day.

God made the trees and the plants. And then without delay,

He made the sun and the moon and He put each star in place.

And everything was good that God decided to create!

In the beginning, God created the heavens and the earth.

And with each passing day God created everything we'd need.

God above, He made them all.

He made everything with care and love.

God had a plan for He even made you and me!

ADAM AND EVE

Adam and Eve were the first man and woman on earth. God gave them a beautiful place to live called *The Garden of Eden*. God allowed them to eat everything in the garden except for the fruit on the tree that grew in the middle. This was the only rule that God wanted Adam and Eve to follow.

One day, when Eve was walking through the garden, a serpent appeared. The serpent said, "God does not want you to eat the fruit from this tree, because you will become as wise as Him and you will know the meaning of good and evil."

Tempted by the serpent's words, Eve took a bite of the fruit and then took it to Adam. They both broke God's only rule. God knew that Adam and Eve had disobeyed Him. He was very sad. He told Adam and Eve to leave the garden.

NOAH

Noah was a good man who obeyed God. But the other people on earth did not listen to Him. So, God told Noah to build a big boat called an ark.

When the ark was finished, Noah took his whole family and two of every kind of animal aboard the ark. Then, God made it rain.

It rained for 40 days and 40 nights. Water covered the earth.
Noah, his family, and all the animals were safe inside the ark.

When the rain stopped, a dove brought Noah an olive branch. This meant that there was land again. Noah knew that it was finally safe to leave the ark.

Noah and his family thanked God when they left the ark. The animals found new homes. God promised never to flood the earth again. He placed a rainbow in the sky to show His promise.

DAVID AND GOLIATH

Jesse was an old man with eight sons. David was his youngest. David was a shepherd boy who liked to play his harp and look after his father's sheep. David also loved God and was very brave.

One day while his older brothers were out in battle, David took them some food and water. Jesse knew his older sons would be hungry. And he wanted to find out how the battle was going.

When David arrived, he saw that a battle between the Israelite and the Philistine armies was about to begin. Someone yelled, "There is Goliath, the giant!" Goliath was over nine feet tall.

Goliath's voice boomed, "Who will fight me?" All of the Israelite soldiers were afraid. But David wasn't. He stepped forward and said to King Saul, "I will fight the giant!" The king agreed. Later that day, David walked out to fight Goliath. The giant became angry when he saw David was just a young boy.

David said, "Even though you fight with a sword and spear, I am not afraid. Because I fight you in the name of the Lord." Then, David placed a stone in his slingshot. He swung it around and around. The stone flew through the air and hit Goliath on his head. Goliath fell down. Everyone cheered because David had defeated the giant.

JONAH

One day God said to Jonah, "I want you to go to the city of Nineveh and tell the people to stop doing bad things." But Jonah was afraid. He did not want to go to Nineveh. So Jonah ran away.

Jonah boarded a ship that would sail far from Nineveh. While he was sleeping, God sent a forceful storm. The sailors were afraid. Jonah knew that the storm was his fault because he did not obey the Lord's command.

Jonah told the sailors to throw him overboard. The sailors did not want to, but the storm was getting worse. As soon as the sailors threw Jonah into the water, the sea grew calm. God sent a big fish to swallow Jonah.

Jonah was inside the big fish for three days and three nights. He was sorry that he did not listen to God. He prayed and asked God for forgiveness. God told the fish to spit out Jonah onto dry land.

God again told Jonah to go to Nineveh. This time, Jonah listened to God. He told the people all about God. They were sorry for all the bad things they had done. The people asked God to forgive them. And He did!

Daniel loved God and prayed to Him every day. King Darius liked Daniel and wanted to put him in charge of his entire kingdom.

But the other leaders did not want Daniel to be in charge. So they came up with a plan. The leaders said, "O King Darius, we think you should make a law. It should say if anyone prays to a god other than your god they will be thrown into the lions' den." The king agreed.

When Daniel heard about the new law, he went home and prayed to God. The other leaders found Daniel praying and told King Darius. The king liked Daniel and was very upset. But he had made the law and ordered Daniel to be thrown into the lions' den.

The next morning, King Darius ran to the lions' den. He found Daniel safe and unharmed. Daniel shouted, "My God sent His angel and He shut the lions' mouths." King Darius was happy and ordered everyone in his kingdom to pray to Daniel's God.

ESTHER

Esther was a beautiful, young Israelite woman. She loved God very much. Esther lived with her cousin Mordecai. He heard that the king of Persia was looking for a wife. Mordecai knew that Esther would make a wonderful queen.

When King Xerxes met Esther, he fell in love. She became his wife. But the king had a wicked advisor named Haman who did not like the Israelite people. So, he asked King Xerxes to make a law. The law would say that all Israelites would be killed because they believed in God. King Xerxes agreed.

Mordecai heard about the new law and warned Esther.
Esther was afraid. King Xerxes did not know that she was
an Israelite. Esther had to think of a plan. Mordecai asked
all the Israelite people to pray for Esther.

Dressed in her royal robes, Esther went to King Xerxes. "What do you want, Queen Esther?" he asked. "I will give you half the kingdom if you want!" Esther replied, "I would like to prepare a banquet for you and your advisor, Haman." The king was pleased and granted Esther's request.

When King Xerxes came to the banquet, Esther told him that she was an Israelite. Esther asked the king to change the law and to not harm any of her people. King Xerxes was angry with Haman. He ordered Haman punished and changed the law. Because of Esther's courage, the Israelite people were saved.

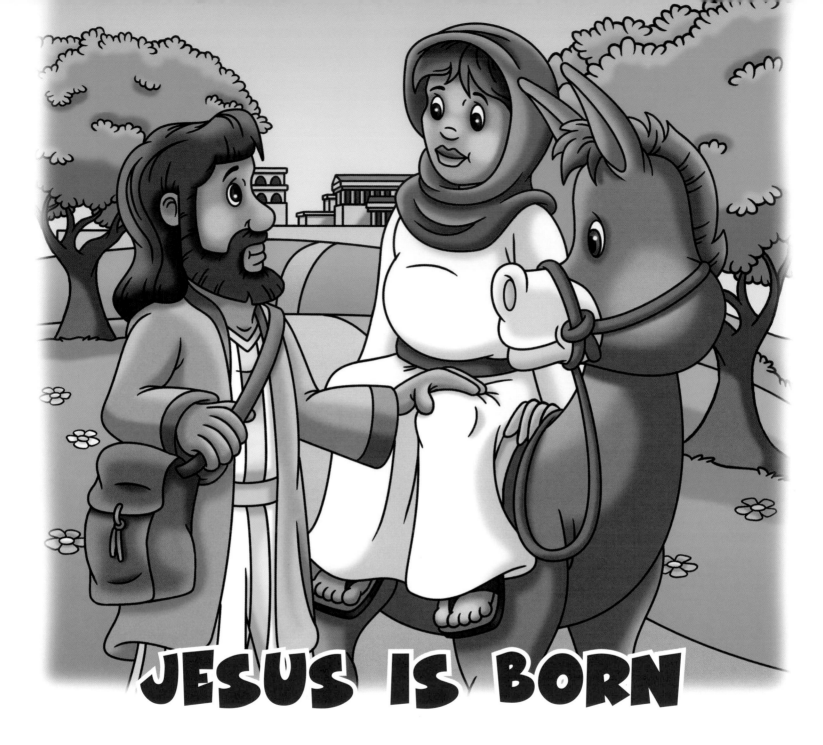

JESUS IS BORN

Caesar Augustus wanted people to be counted in their hometowns. So Joseph and Mary began their long journey to Bethlehem. Mary rode a donkey because she was going to have a baby. When they finally arrived in Bethlehem, there was no place to stay. Every inn in town was full.

Mary was ready to have her baby. A very kind innkeeper
said that they could stay in his stable with the animals.
That night, Mary gave birth to God's son, Jesus. She
wrapped him in cloths and placed Him in a manger.

There were shepherds in the fields nearby. An angel appeared to the shepherds and said, "Do not be afraid. I bring you good news of great joy. Today, in the town of Bethlehem, a Savior has been born."

The shepherds went to Bethlehem. They found Jesus lying in a manger. They praised God for sending His only Son to earth. Jesus was God's greatest gift to us all!

ZACCHAEUS

Zacchaeus was a tax collector in the city of Jericho. He collected money from people who sold clothing, pottery, food, and other things in the city. But Zacchaeus was not an honest man. He kept some of the money he collected.

Zacchaeus learned that Jesus was coming to Jericho. He wanted to hear Jesus speak. But Zacchaeus was a little man and would not be able to see Jesus over the crowd. So Zacchaeus climbed up into a sycamore tree.

When Jesus walked by the tree, He looked up and said,
"Zacchaeus, come down. I must stay at your house today."
Zacchaeus climbed down from the tree and ran home to
get ready for Jesus.

When Jesus arrived at his house, Zacchaeus told Jesus he was sorry for all the wrong things he had done. "I will give half of everything I have to the poor," said Zacchaeus. That made Jesus very happy and He blessed Zacchaeus.

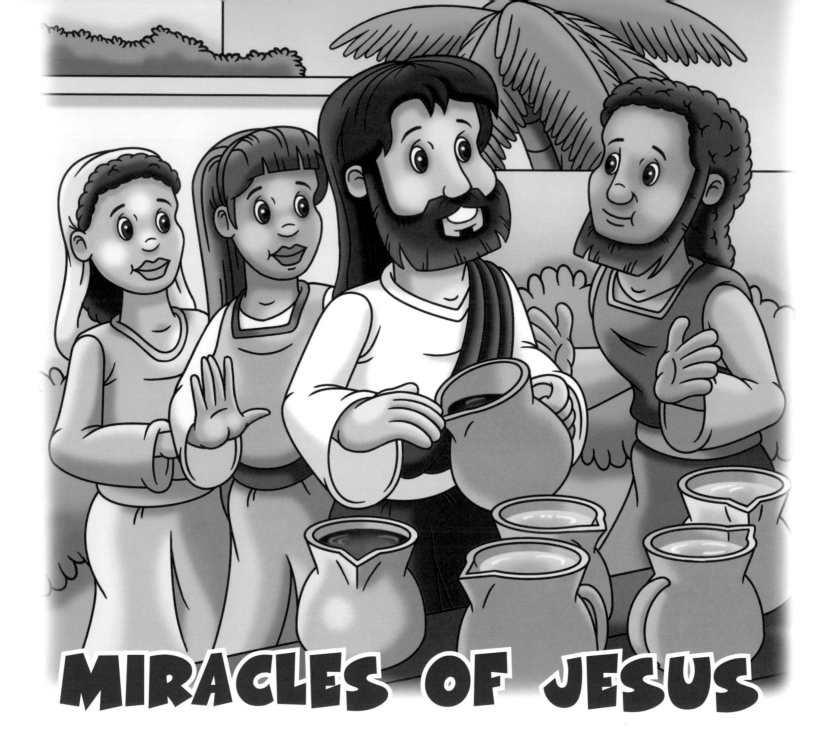

MIRACLES OF JESUS

One day, Jesus and His followers were invited to a wedding celebration. Wedding feasts lasted for many days then. During the party, the bride and groom ran out of wine. Jesus took six large water jugs and turned the water into wine. This was Jesus' first miracle.

Jesus talked to many people about the Word of God. He healed many sick people and helped a blind man to see. One day, with only five loaves of bread and two fish, Jesus was able to feed five thousand people. He performed many miracles as He walked from town to town.

Mary and Martha were friends with Jesus. Jesus cried when their brother Lazarus died. Jesus went to the tomb and had the stone taken away. He called out in a loud voice, "Lazarus, come out!" Lazarus had been dead for four days, but Jesus made Lazarus live again.

Jesus loved to teach people about God. He said, "I am the way and the truth and the life. No one comes to the Father except through me." Some people did not understand Jesus. They nailed Him to a cross. Jesus told them that even though He would die, He would be back. Jesus died on the cross.

Three days later, Jesus was alive again. God loves us so much that he sent His only Son to earth to die for our sins. God's gift is free to all who believe.

JESUS IS ALIVE

After Jesus died, a man named Joseph took Jesus' body and wrapped it in clean cloths. Joseph placed Jesus' body in a tomb. Then, Joseph rolled a huge stone in front of it. Soldiers guarded the tomb to make sure no one would move Jesus' body.

After three days, two women named Mary visited the tomb
of Jesus. All of the sudden, there was a loud earthquake.
An angel had appeared and moved the huge stone
aside. The soldiers were afraid and ran away.

The angel said to the women, "Do not be afraid. I know that you are looking for Jesus. He is not in the tomb! Jesus is alive again, just like He said He would be!"

The women were so excited. They quickly ran to tell Jesus'
followers the great news. "Jesus is alive! Jesus is alive!" they
shouted. All of Jesus' followers praised God.